SONGS OF
England

45 favourite songs for voice and piano

Arranged by Margery Hargest Jones

Boosey & Hawkes Music Publishers Ltd
www.boosey.com

Cover design by Peter Hobbs
Layout by Sue Clarke
Music engraved by Jack Thompson
Chord symbols have been included above the melody line.
A transposed version is given below the stave in smaller
type where the chords are awkward for guitarists.
The chord symbols suggested have been chosen to suit the
solo melody and do not always correspond to the
harmony of the keyboard accompaniment.

Contents

Introduction

The national songs of England have a rich and varied heritage. Many of the songs are ballads – narrative poems on popular themes, often focusing on just one or two central characters. *Barbara Allen* and *The Wraggle Taggle Gypsies* are both fine examples of this form, each one telling a story through a poem made up of four-line stanzas. They are also typical in that many different versions of the songs are found throughout the British Isles and North America.

O Waly Waly is another song that can be found in various parts of the country. It was collected in Somerset by Cecil Sharp (1859-1924), but shows signs of having some Scottish origins. It is often impossible to be certain where a song has its roots, as even the mention of a specific location in the poem is no proof that the song was composed there: performers of folk songs frequently altered words to make them more relevant to a particular area.

The English seafaring tradition is also reflected in this collection. There are songs of farewell, such as *The Rio Grande* and *The Leaving of Liverpool*, while others are sailors' work songs, or shanties. The best known of these is, of course, *The Drunken Sailor*, but another one included here is the comic song, *The Drummer and the Cook*.

England also has a number of stirring, patriotic songs. These tend to date from the days of British empire-building and were generally by well-known composers, such as William Boyce (1711-1779) (*Heart of Oak*) and Thomas Arne (1710-1778) (*Rule Britannia*). There are also songs that are particularly associated with the army: *The British Grenadiers* and *The Girl I Left Behind Me*.

While there are settings of poems by well-known authors, notably Shakespeare, Ben Jonson and Tennyson, most of the poems are anonymous and were passed on in the oral tradition for generations before finding their way into print. A great debt is owed therefore to collectors who often saved songs from extinction. Included here are some of the songs collected by Cecil Sharp, the Reverend Sabine Baring-Gould, Frank Kidson, William Chappell and Sir Richard Runciman Terry.

Background notes have been included to many of the songs to place them in context in English social and musical history.

The accompaniments in this book have deliberately been kept simple. The melody line is always included in the piano part, so that the songs may be played as keyboard solos as well as with the voice.

The Bailiff's Daughter

Words and music anon.

1. There was a youth and a well be-lov-éd youth, And he was a squire's son; He loved the Bai-liff's daugh-ter dear, That lived in Is-ling-ton.

2 But when his friends did understand
His fond and foolish mind,
They sent him up to fair London,
An apprentice for to bind.

3 Now when seven years had passed away,
And ne'er his love could find,
The bailiff's daughter set her heart,
To prove his secret mind.

4 Now as she went along the high road,
Through the weather hot and dry,
She sat her down on a green bank,
And her true love came riding by.

5 She started up with colour red,
And held his bridle rein;
'One penny, one penny, kind sir,' she said,
'Will ease me of much pain.'

6 'Before I give you a penny, fair maid,
Pray tell me where you were born?'
'At Islington, kind sir,' she said,
'And I left at yester morn.'

7 'I prithee, maiden, tell to me,
O tell me whether you know
The Bailiff's daughter of Islington,
Is she dead long, long ago?'

8 'O stay, O stay, thou goodly youth,
She standeth by your side,
She is here alive, she is not dead,
But ready to be your bride.'

Barbara Allen

Words and music anon.

This ballad is one of the most enduringly popular, both in England and Scotland. It is mentioned by Samuel Pepys in his diary on 2 January 1666. It has been set to various tunes, but the familiar melody we know was first printed in William Chappell's *National English Airs from Tradition* in 1838.

1 In Scar-let town, where I was born, There was a fair maid dwell-in', Made ev-'ry youth cry 'Well-a-way!' Her name was Bar - bara Al-len. Al-len.

2 All in the merry month of May,
  When green buds they were swellin',
  Young Jemmy Grove on his death-bed lay,
  For love of Barbara Allen.

3 So slowly, slowly she came up,
  And slowly she came nigh him,
  And all she said, when she came there:
  'Young man, I think you're dying!'

4 When he was dead and laid in grave,
  Her heart was struck with sorrow;
  'O mother, mother, make my bed,
  For I shall die tomorrow.'

5 'Farewell!' she said, 'ye maidens all,
  And shun the fault I fell in;
  Henceforth take warning by the fall
  Of cruel Barbara Allen.'

Begone, Dull Care!

Words anon.
17th century air

1. Be - gone! dull care, I pri-thee, be - gone from me, Be-gone! dull care, You and I shall ne - ver a - gree. Long time hast thou been tar - rying here, And fain thou wouldst me kill, But i'

faith, dull care,_____ Thou ne - ver shall have__ thy will._____

2 Too much care
  Will make a man turn grey,
  And too much care
  Will turn an old man to clay.
  My wife shall dance and I will sing,
  So merrily pass the day,
  For I hold it one of the wisest things
  To drive dull care away.

Billy Boy

Words and music traditional

This is from Northumberland and is a shanty, or sailor's work song, sung while pulling together on a rope and so helping to secure rhythmic unanimity. The shantyman sang the tune, the rest joining in the chorus. It was collected by Sir Richard Runciman Terry.

Nan - cy kit - tl'd me fan - cy Oh me charm - in' Bill - y Boy.

2 Is she fit to be your wife
   Billy Boy, Billy Boy?
   Is she fit to be your wife, me Billy Boy?
   She's as fit to be me wife
   As the fork is to the knife
   And me Nancy kittl'd me fancy
   Oh me charmin' Billy Boy.

3 Can she cook a bit o' steak
   Billy Boy, Billy Boy?
   Can she cook a bit o' steak, me Billy Boy?
   She can cook a bit o' steak,
   Aye, and myek a gairdle cake
   Chorus

4 Can she myek an Irish stew
   Billy Boy, Billy Boy?
   Can she myek an Irish stew, me Billy Boy?
   She can myek an Irish stew,
   Aye, and 'Singin' Hinnies' too,
   Chorus

Blaydon Races

Words by George Ridley
Music anon.

This song was made popular by a Tyneside comedian called J.C. Scatter (James Cosgrove). The famous sporting event that it describes was last held in September 1916.

2 We flew past Armstrong's factory
  And up by the 'Robin Adair',
  Just gannin' down by the railway bridge,
  The bus wheel flew off there.
  The lasses lost their crinolines
  And the veils that hid their faces.
  I got two black eyes and a broken nose,
  Gannin' to the Blaydon Races.
       And it's O my lads,
       You should have seen us gannin',
       Passin' the folks along the road,
       Just as they were stannin';
       There were lots o' lads and lasses there,
       All wi' smilin' faces,
       Gannin' along the Scotswood Road
       To see the Blaydon Races.

3 When we got the wheel put on,
  Away we went again,
  But some that had their noses broke,
  They went back over home.
  Some went to the dispensary
  And some to Doctor Gibbs's
  And some went to the infirmary
  To mend their broken ribses.
       Chorus

4 Now when they got to Paradise
  There was bonny game begun,
  There was four and twenty on the bus,
  Man, how they danced and sung.
  They called on me to sing a song,
  I sang them 'Paddy Fagan',
  I danced a jig and I swung me twig,
  The day I went to Blaydon.
       Chorus

15

Blow, Blow thou Winter Wind

Words by Shakespeare
Music by Thomas Arne

The words are taken from Shakespeare's 'joyous comedy', *As You Like It*, adapted by Thomas Arne for this setting.

16

2 Freeze, freeze, thou bitter sky,
  Thou dost not bite so nigh,
  Thou dost not bite so nigh
  As benefits forgot;
  Tho' thou the waters warp,
  Thy sting is not so sharp,
  Thy sting is not so sharp
  As friends remember'd not,
  Thy sting is not so sharp
  As friends remember'd not,
  As friends remember'd not.

Bobby Shaftoe

Words and music anon.

He's my ain for e - ver mair, Bon - ny Bob - by Shaf - toe.

3 Bobby Shaftoe's tall and slim,
   He's always dressed so neat and trim,
   The lasses they all keek at him!
   Bonny Bobby Shaftoe.

4 Bobby Shaftoe's gett'n a bairn
   For to dangle in his airm,
   In his airm and on his knee,
   Bonny Bobby Shaftoe.

5 Bobby Shaftoe's been to sea,
   Silver buckles on his knee;
   He's come back and married me,
   Bonny Bobby Shaftoe.

The British Grenadiers

Words 17th century
Music early 18th century

The version of this song that is known today contains an allusion to the Battle of Waterloo (1815), where the Grenadier Regiment of Foot Guards defeated the Grenadiers of the Imperial Guard. It is the Regimental March of the Grenadier Guards.

tow, row, row, row, row, row, to the Bri-tish Gren-a - diers.

2 None of those ancient heroes e'er saw a cannon-ball,
   Or knew the force of powder to slay their foes withal;
   But our brave boys do know it, and banish all their fears;
      With a tow, row, row, row, row, row, to the British Grenadiers.

3 Whene'er we are commanded to storm the palisades,
   Our leaders march with fuses, and we with hand-grenades,
   We throw them from the glacis about the enemies' ears;
      Sing tow, row, row, row, row, row, to the British Grenadiers.

4 And when the siege is over, we to the town repair;
   The townsmen cry, 'Hurrah, boys, here comes a Grenadier,
   Here come the Grenadiers, my boys, who know no doubts or fears!'
      With a tow, row, row, row, row, row, to the British Grenadiers.

5 Then let us fill a bumper and drink a health to those
   Who carry caps and pouches, and wear the loupéd clothes;
   May they and their commanders live happy all their years,
      With a tow, row, row, row, row, row, for the British Grenadiers.

The Candlelight Fisherman

Words by Phil Hamond and Peter Kennedy

The title was once used widely to mean a lazy fisherman – as the words clearly illustrate!

With movement

1. Oh me dad was a fish-er-man bold And he lived till he grew old, For he o-pens the pane and he pops out the flame Just to see how the wind do blow. If the flame don't flick-er 'e'd know That there's not e-nough wind do

blow, But if that sil-ly old flame blow out Then there's too much wind to go.

2 And often he'd say to me,
You'd be wise before you go,
Do you open the pane and pop out the flame
Just to see how the wind do blow.
If the flame don't flicker 'e'd know
That there's not enough wind do blow,
But if that silly old flame blow out
Then there's too much wind to go.

3 When the north wind rough did blow,
Then I lay right snug below;
But I opens the pane and I pop out the flame
Just to see how the wind do blow.
Chorus

4 When the wind come out of the east,
You'll be looking for snow and sleet;
But I opens the pane and I pop out the flame
Just to see how the wind do blow.
Chorus

5 When the wind's back into the west
That'll come in rough at best;
But I opens the pane and I pop out the flame
Just to see how the wind do blow.
Chorus

6 When the south wind soft do blow
It's then I love to go;
And I opens the pane and I pop out the flame
Just to see how the wind do blow.
Chorus

7 And my poor wife say to me,
'We shall starve if you don't go;'
So I opens the pane and I pop out the flame
Just to see how the wind do blow.
Chorus

8 Now all you fishermen bold,
If you live till you grow old,
Do you open the pane and pop out the flame
Just to see how the wind do blow.
Chorus

Come Lasses and Lads

Words and music anon.

This 17th century air is still used for dancing around the maypole.

2 'You're out!' says Dick; 'Not I!' says Nick,
''Twas the fiddler played it wrong.'
''Tis true!' says Hugh, and so says Sue,
And so says everyone.
The fiddler then began
To play the tune again,
And ev'ry girl did trip it, trip it, trip it to the men,
And ev'ry girl did trip it, trip it, trip it to the men.

3 'Goodnight!' says Harry; 'Goodnight!' says Mary;
'Goodnight!' says Poll to John.
'Goodnight!' says Sue to her sweetheart, Hugh,
'Goodnight!' says ev'ryone.
Some walked and some did run;
Some loitered on the way,
And bound themselves, by kisses twelve, to meet the next holiday,
And bound themselves, by kisses twelve, to meet the next holiday.

Dashing Away With the Smoothing Iron

This Somerset folk song was collected by Cecil Sharp.

Joyfully

1. 'Twas on a Mon-day morn-ing, When I be-held my dar-ling, She looked so neat and charm-ing In ev-'ry high de-gree;_____ She looked so neat and nim-ble, O, A-wash-ing of her lin-en, O, *Dash-ing a-way with the smooth-ing iron,*

Dash-ing a-way with the smooth-ing iron, She stole my heart a - way.____ way.____

2 'Twas on a Tuesday morning,
  When I beheld my darling,
  She looked so neat and charming
  In ev'ry high degree;
  She looked so neat and nimble, O,
  A-hanging out her linen, O,
    Dashing away with the smoothing iron,
    Dashing away with the smoothing iron,
    She stole my heart away.

3 'Twas on a Wednesday morning, *etc.*
  A-starching of her linen, O,
    Chorus

4 'Twas on a Thursday morning, *etc.*
  An-ironing of her linen, O,
    Chorus

5 'Twas on a Friday morning, *etc.*
  A-folding of her linen, O,
    Chorus

6 'Twas on a Saturday morning, *etc.*
  An-airing of her linen, O,
    Chorus

7 'Twas on a Sunday morning, *etc.*
  A-wearing of her linen, O,
    Chorus

The Derby Ram

Music 18th century

This is obviously a long and 'tall' tale and could have many more verses than are given here. The ram features in the coat of arms of Derby and in the emblem of Derby football club.

Humorously

I was go-ing to Der-by, sir, U-pon a mar-ket day,___ I___ met the fin-est ram, sir, That e-ver was fed on hay. *In-* *-deed, sir, it's the truth sir, For I ne-ver was taught to lie, And___*

CHORUS

1. As

if you go to Der - by, sir, You may eat a bit of the pie._____

2 This ram was fat behind, sir,
This ram was fat before,
This ram was ten yards high, sir,
Indeed he was no more.
> *Indeed, sir, it's the truth, sir,*
> *For I never was taught to lie,*
> *And if you go to Derby, sir,*
> *You may eat a bit of the pie.*

3 The wool upon his back, sir,
Reached up into the sky,
The eagles build their nests there,
For I heard the young ones cry.
Chorus

4 The wool upon his tail, sir,
Was three yards and an ell,
Of it they made a rope, sir,
To pull the parish bell.
Chorus

5 The space between the horns, sir,
Was as far as man could reach,
And there they built a pulpit,
But no-one in it preached.
Chorus

6 This ram had four legs to walk upon,
This ram had four legs to stand,
And every leg he had, sir,
Stood on an acre of land.
Chorus

7 Now the man that fed the ram, sir,
He fed him twice a day,
And each time that he fed him, sir,
He ate a rick of hay.
Chorus

8 The man that killed the ram, sir,
Was up to his knees in blood,
And the boy that held the pail, sir,
Was carried away in the flood.
Chorus

Drink to Me Only With Thine Eyes

Words by Ben Jonson
Music anon.

Drink to me only with thine eyes is the first line of the poem *To Celia* from *The Forrest* published in 1616. The tune first occurs in about 1770 when it was published as a glee.

1. Drink to me only with_ thine eyes And I_ will pledge with mine;_ Or leave a kiss with- in_ the cup_ And I'll_ not ask for wine._ The thirst that from the soul_ doth rise Doth ask a drink di - vine;_

30

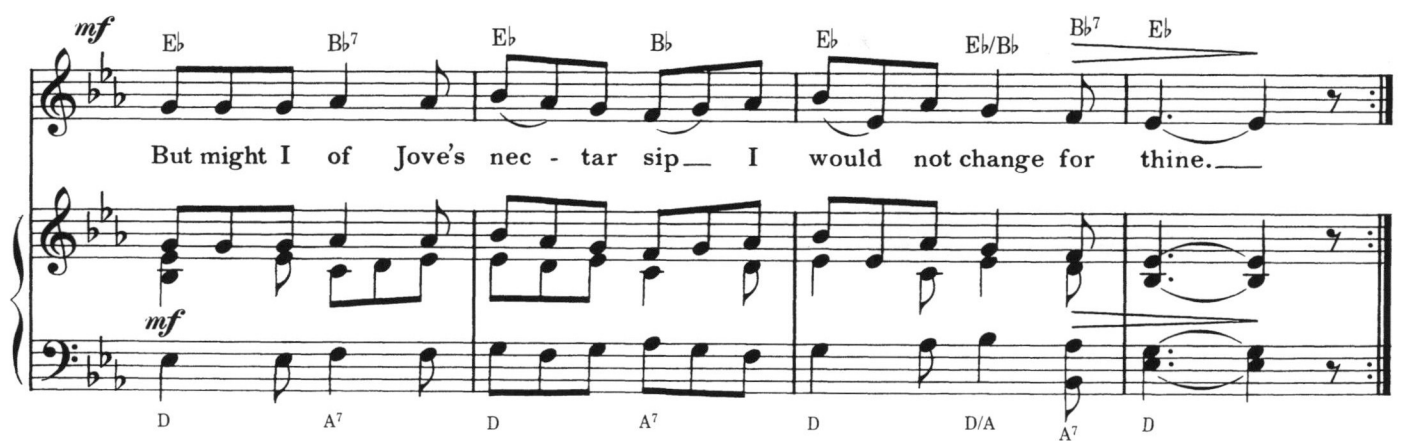

But might I of Jove's nec - tar sip___ I would not change for thine.___

2 I sent thee late a rosy wreath,
  Not so much honouring thee,
  As giving it a hope that there
  It could not wither'd be.
  But thou thereon didst only breathe
  And sent'st it back to me;
  Since when it grows, and smells, I swear
  Not of itself, but thee.

The Drummer and the Cook

This may have been a music hall song, but when it was collected by Sir Richard Runciman Terry it was being sung on board the Blyth brig *Northumberland* as a windlass or capstan shanty. Terry wrote verses 2 to 7 having heard only the first verse from the captain of the ship.

1. O there was a lit-tle drum-mer And he loved a one eyed cook, And he loved her, O he loved her Though she had a cock-eyed look, *With her one eye in the pot, And the t'oth-er up the chim-ney, With a bow - wow - wow, Fal - lal the dow-a-did-dy Bow-wow-wow. Bow-wow-wow.*

(Capo on 3rd fret)

2 When this couple went a-courtin'
  For to walk along the shore,
  Sez the drummer to the cookie,
  'You're the gel that I adore.'
        With her one eye in the pot,
        And the t'other up the chimney,
        With a bow-wow-wow,
        Fal-lal the dow-a-diddy
        Bow-wow-wow.

3 When this couple went a-courtin'
  For to walk along the pier,
  Sez the cookie to the drummer,
  'An' I love you too, my dear.'
        Chorus

4 Sez the drummer to the cookie,
  'Ain't the weather fine today?'
  Sez the cookie to the drummer,
  'Is that all ye got to say?'
        Chorus

5 Sez the drummer to the cookie,
  'Will I buy the weddin' ring?'
  Sez the cookie, 'Now you're talkin',
  That would be the very thing.'
        Chorus

6 Sez the drummer to the cookie,
  'Will ye name the weddin' day?'
  Sez the cookie, 'We'll be married
  In the merry month of May.'
        Chorus

7 When they went to church to say, 'I will,'
  The drummer got a nark,
  For her one eye gliffed the Parson
  And the t'other killed the Clerk.
        Chorus

Early One Morning

Words and music anon.

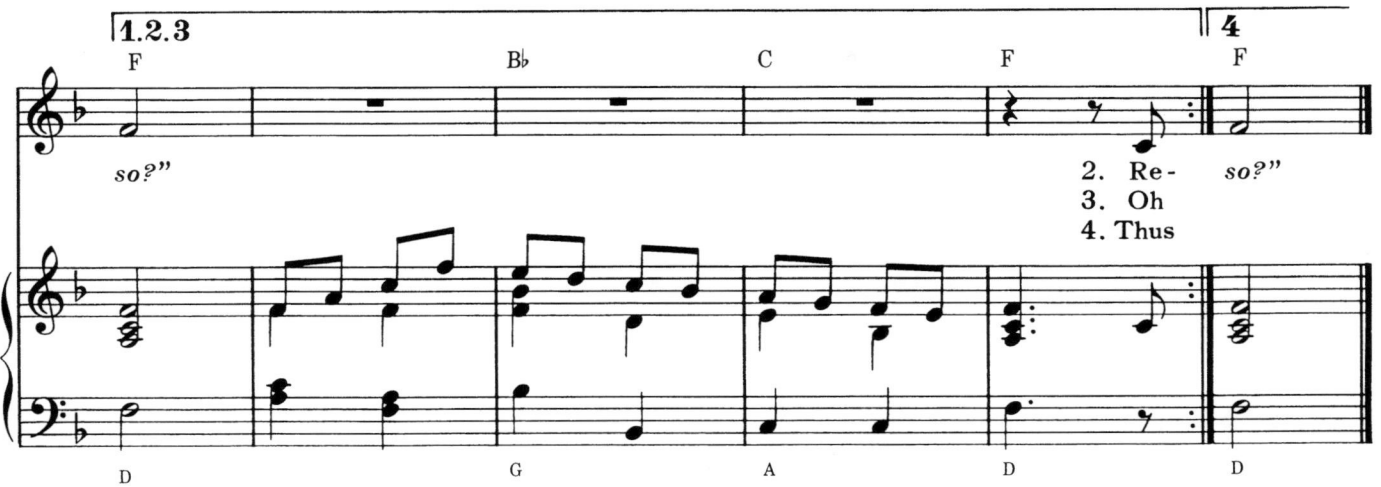

2 'Remember the vows that you made to your Mary,
Remember the bow'r where you vowed to be true.'
   'Oh! don't deceive me, oh! never leave me,
   How could you use a poor maiden so?'

3 'Oh gay is the garland and fresh are the roses
I've culled from the garden to bind on thy brow.'
   Chorus

4 Thus sang the poor maiden, her sorrow bewailing,
Thus sang the poor maid in the valley below.
   Chorus

The Girl I Left Behind Me

Words 18th century
Music anon.

The words of this song can be traced back to the mid-18th century. Around 1759 there were many encampments along the south coast of England anticipating French invasion. The tune, which is anonymous, is sometimes known as *Brighton Camp*. It is still played by the British Army on occasions of departure.

Firmly, with movement

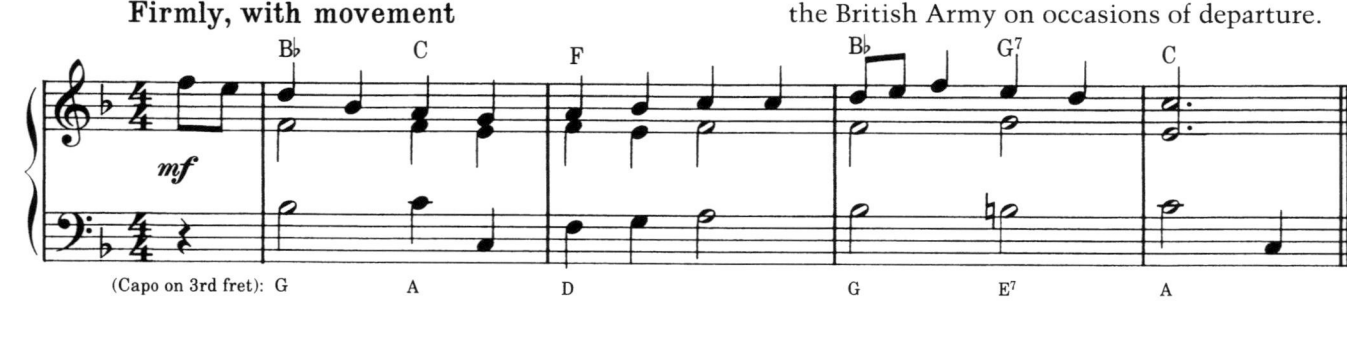

(Capo on 3rd fret): G   A   D   G   E⁷   A

1. I'm lone-some since I crossed the hill, And o'er the moor and val-ley, Such

hea-vy thoughts my heart do fill, Since part-ing with my Sal-ly. I

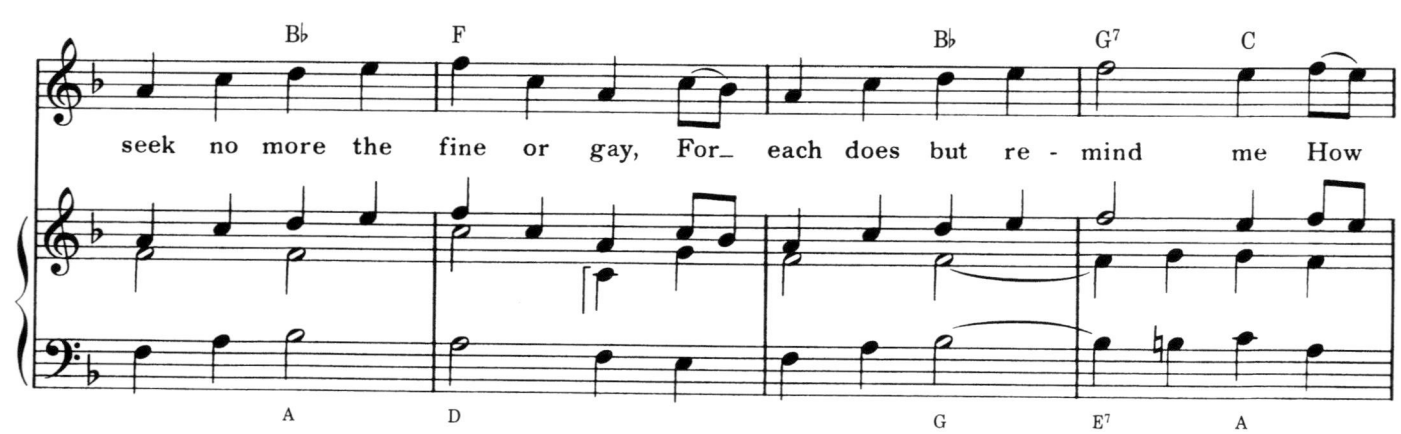

seek no more the fine or gay, For each does but re-mind me How

swift the_ hours did pass a - way With the girl_ I left be - hind me.

2 Oh ne'er shall I forget the night,
The stars were bright above me,
And gently lent their silv'ry light,
When first she vowed to love me.
But now I'm bound to Brighton camp,
Kind heaven then pray guide me,
And send me safely back again
To the girl I've left behind me.

3 Her golden hair in ringlets fair,
Her eyes like diamonds shining,
Her slender waist, with carriage chaste,
May leave the swan repining.
Ye gods above! Oh hear my prayer,
To my beauteous fair to bind me,
And send me safely back again
To the girl I've left behind me.

Greensleeves

Words and music 16th century

Shakespeare mentions this old and much-loved tune twice in *The Merry Wives of Windsor* (1597-1600). It probably dates from the mid-16th century.

Flowingly

(Capo on 1st fret): G

1. A - las, my love you do me wrong To cast me off dis - cour - teous - ly, And

I have lov - éd you so long, De - light - ing in your com - pan - y.

CHORUS

Green - sleeves was all my joy, Green - sleeves was my de - light,

2 I have been ready at your hand
  To grant whatever you would crave;
  I have both wagéd life and land,
  Your love and goodwill for to have.
     Greensleeves was all my joy,
     Greensleeves was my delight,
     Greensleeves was my heart of gold,
     And who but my lady Greensleeves.

3 I bought thee kerchers for thy head
  That were wrought fine and gallantly;
  I kept thee both at board and bed,
  Which cost my purse well favouredly.
     Chorus

4 I bought thee petticoats of the best,
  The cloth so fine as fine might be;
  I gave thee jewels for thy chest,
  And all this cost I spent on thee.
     Chorus

5 Well I will pray to God on high
  That thou my constancy mayst see,
  And that yet once before I die
  Thou wilt vouchsafe to love me.
     Chorus

Heart of Oak

Words by David Garrick
Music by William Boyce

This highly patriotic song comes from a pantomime, *Harlequins Invasion,* written in 1759. An Americanised version was composed in 1768 and became very popular as *The Liberty Song.*

Strongly, with spirit

1. Come, cheer up, my lads, 'tis to glo - ry we steer, To add some-thing more to this won - der-ful year; To____ hon - our we call you, not press you like slaves, For who are so free as the sons of the waves? *Heart of*

2 We ne'er see our foes but we wish them to stay,
They never see us but they wish us away;
If they run, why we follow, and run them ashore,
And if they won't fight us, we cannot do more.
> *Heart of oak are our ships, heart of oak are our men,*
> *We always are ready; steady, boys, steady!*
> *We'll fight and we'll conquer again and again.*

3 Still Britain shall triumph, her ships plough the sea,
Her standard be justice, her watchword 'Be free',
Then cheer up, my lads, with one heart let us sing,
Our soldiers, our sailors, our statesmen and King.
> *Chorus*

I Gave My Love a Cherry

Words and music anon.

This kind of riddle song depends on the correct answers being given to win the hand of the lady, so it becomes a battle of wits between the two people.

2 How can there be a cherry that has no stone?
  How can there be a chicken that has no bone?
  How can there be a ring that has no end?
  How can there be a baby that's no cryen?

3 A cherry when it's blooming, it has no stone.
  A chicken when it's pipping, it has no bone.
  A ring when it's rolling, it has no end.
  A baby when it's sleeping, there's no cryen.

Johnny Todd

This children's rhyme and game was collected in Liverpool near the end of the l9th century by Frank Kidson. He included it in his *Traditional Tunes* (1891) and said, 'The air is somewhat pleasing, and the words appear old, though some blanks caused by the reciter's memory have had to be filled up.'

1. John-ny Todd he took a no-tion For to sail the o-cean wide, And he left his true love be-hind him, Weep-ing by the Li-ver-pool tide.

2 For a week she wept full sorely,
  Tore her hair and wrung her hands,
  Then she met with another sailor
  Walking on the Liverpool sands.

3 'O fair maid, why are you weeping
  For your Johnny gone to sea?
  If you wed with me tomorrow
  I will kind and constant be.'

4 'I will buy sheets and blankets,
  I'll buy you a wedding ring,
  You shall have a gilded cradle
  For to rock your baby in.'

5 Johnny Todd came back from sailing,
  Sailing o'er the ocean wide,
  But he found that his fair and false one
  Was another sailor's bride.

6 All young men who go a-sailing
  Or to fight the foreign foe,
  Don't you leave your love like Johnny,
  Marry her before you go.

The Keel Row

Words and music anon.

This song is closely associated with Newcastle and Tyneside generally; although its first appearance in print was in *A Collection of Favourite Scots Tunes* in Edinburgh, circa 1770. Keel means a boat and the Tyneside words represent a lassie singing 'Weel may the keel row, that my laddie's in.'

2 Oh! who is like my Johnny,
  Sae leish, sae blithe, sae bonny,
  He's foremost o' the mony
  Keel lads o' coaly Tyne.
        Weel may the keel row,
        The keel row, the keel row,
        Weel may the keel row,
        That my laddie's in.

3 He'll set or row sae tightly,
  Or in the dance sae sprightly,
  He'll cut and shuffle sightly,
  'Tis true, were he not mine.
        Chorus

4 He wears a blue bonnet,
  Blue bonnet, blue bonnet,
  He wears a blue bonnet,
  A dimple's in his chin.
        Chorus

The Leaving of Liverpool

Words and music 19th century

This is a sailor's farewell song, possibly from around 1860, when clipper ships made the long and dangerous journeys from Liverpool to America.

Smoothly

1. Fare thee well, the Prin - ce's__ Land - ing Stage, Ri - ver Mer - sey, fare thee well, For I'm bound for Ca - li - for - ni - a, It's a place that I know right well. So__ fare thee well, my own true love, And when

I re-turn, u-ni-ted we will be, _____ It's not the leav-ing of Li-ver-pool that

grieves _____ me, But, my dar-ling, when I think of thee.

2 Well, I'm bound for California,
By way of the stormy Cape Horn,
But you know I'll write you a letter, my love,
When I am homeward bound.
So fare thee well, my own true love,
And when I return, united we will be;
It's not the leaving of Liverpool that
grieves me,
But, my darling, when I think of thee.

3 I have shipped on a Yankee clipper ship,
Davy Crockett is her name,
And Burgess is the captain of her,
And they say that she's a floating shame.
Chorus

4 Oh the tug is waiting at the pier head,
To take us down the stream,
Our sails are unfurled and our anchor is
stowed,
So fare thee well again.
Chorus

5 Fare thee well to Lower Frederick Street,
Anson Terrace and Old Parkee Lane,
For I know it will be some long, long time
Before I see you again.
Chorus

The Lincolnshire Poacher

Words and music anon.

my de-light on a shin - y night, In the sea - son of the year. Yes, 'tis

my de-light on a shin - y night, In the sea - son of the year.

2 As me and my companions were setting up a snare,
   'Twas then we spied the gamekeeper, for him we did not care,
   For we can wrestle and fight, my boys, and jump out anywhere.
   Oh, 'tis my delight on a shiny night,
   In the season of the year.
   Yes 'tis my delight on a shiny night,
   In the season of the year.

3 As me and my companions were setting four or five,
   And, taking on 'em up again, we caught a hare alive,
   We took the hare alive, my boys, and through the woods did steer.
   Chorus

4 I threw him on my shoulder, and then we trudgéd home,
   We took him to a neighbour's house and sold him for a crown,
   We sold him for a crown, my boys, I did not tell you where.
   Chorus

5 Success to every gentleman that lives in Lincolnshire,
   Success to every poacher that wants to sell a hare,
   Bad luck to every gamekeeper that will not sell his deer.
   Chorus

Maa Bonny Lad

Words and music anon.

This traditional Northumbrian folk song conveys the sadness of the event of a lover being lost at sea.

2 Yes, aa'v seen yor bonny lad,
  'Twas on the sea aa spied him,
  His grave is green but not wi' grass;
  And thou'lt never lie aside him.

The Mermaid

Words and music early 19th century

This song was noted down by the collector William Chappell (1808-88) in 1840 from the singing of Mr Charles Sloman.

Vigorously

1. One Fri - day morn when we set sail And our ship not far from land, We there did es - py a fair pret - ty maid, With a comb and a glass in her hand, her hand, her hand, With a comb and a glass in her hand.

While the

ra - ging seas__ did__ roar, And the storm - y winds did__ blow, And__ we jol - ly sai - lor boys were up,__ up a - loft, And the land - lub - bers ly - ing down be - low, be - low, be - low, And the land - lub - bers ly - ing down be - low.

2 Then up spoke the captain of our gallant ship,
Who at once our peril did see,
'I have married a wife in fair London town,
And this night she a widow will be.'
    While the raging seas did roar,
    And the stormy winds did blow,
    And we jolly sailor boys were up, up
        aloft,
    And the land-lubbers lying down below,
        below, below,
    And the land-lubbers lying down below.

3 And then up spoke the little cabin boy,
And a fair hair'd boy was he,
'I've a father and mother in fair Portsmouth
    town,
And this night they will weep for me.'
        Chorus

4 Then three times round went our gallant
    ship,
And three times round went she;
For the want of a lifeboat they all went down,
As she sank to the bottom of the sea.
        Chorus

The Miller of the Dee

Music 17th century

This tune is found in ballad-operas from 1728 onwards and Arne included it in *Love in a Village,* first performed in Covent Garden in 1762.

be,_____ "I care for no-bo-dy, no, not I, If no-bo-dy cares for

me."

1.2.3 ǀǀ *last time*

2 'I live by the mill, she is to me
Like parent, child and wife;
I would not change my station
For any other in life.
No lawyer, surgeon or doctor
E'er had a groat from me;
I care for nobody, no, not I,
If nobody cares for me.'

3 When spring begins its merry career,
Oh! how his heart grows gay;
No summer drought alarms his fears,
Nor winter's sad decay;
No foresight mars the miller's joy,
Who's wont to sing and say,
'Let others toil from year to year,
I live from day to day.'

4 Then, like the miller, bold and free,
Let us rejoice and sing;
The days of youth are made for glee,
And time is on the wing.
This song shall pass from me to thee
And round this jovial ring,
And all in heart and voice agree
To sing, 'Long live the King.'

My Bonnie is Over the Ocean

Words and music anon.

2 O blow, ye winds, over the ocean,
O blow, ye winds, over the sea,
O blow, ye winds, over the ocean,
And bring back my Bonnie to me.
Bring back, bring back
Bring back my Bonnie to me, to me;
Bring back, bring back,
O bring back my Bonnie to me.

3 Last night as I lay on my pillow,
Last night as I lay on my bed,
Last night as I lay on my pillow,
I dreamt that my Bonnie was dead.
Chorus

O Waly Waly

This song was collected in Somerset by Cecil Sharp, but seems also to be of Scottish origin. 'Waly' is Scottish for 'alas'.

2 O, down in the meadows the other day,
  A-gath'ring flowers both fine and gay,
  A-gath'ring flowers both red and blue,
  I little thought what love can do.

3 I leaned my back up against some oak,
  Thinking that he was a trusty tree;
  But first he bended and then he broke,
  And so did my false love to me.

4 A ship there is and she sails the sea,
  She's loaded deep as deep can be,
  But not so deep as the love I'm in;
  I know not if I sink or swim.

5 O, love is handsome and love is fine,
  And love's a jewel while it is new,
  But when it is old, it groweth cold,
  And fades away like morning dew.

The Oak and the Ash

Words and music anon.

bon - ny i - vy tree, They_ flour - ish at home In my own coun - try.

2 While sadly I roam,
  I regret my dear home,
  Where lads and young lasses are making the hay;
  The merry bells ring,
  And the birds sweetly sing,
  And maidens and meadows are pleasant and gay.
      Oh! the oak and the ash
      And the bonny ivy tree,
      They flourish at home
      In my own country.

3 No doubt, did I please,
  I could marry with ease;
  Where maidens are fair many lovers will come;
  But he whom I wed
  Must be north country bred,
  And carry me back to my north country home.
      Chorus

On Ilkley Moor Baht 'at

Words and music anon.

This old North Country folk song 'On Ilkley Moor without a hat' is a favourite Yorkshire song.

2 Tha's been a-coortin' Mary Jane,
    On Ilkley Moor baht 'at.
Tha's been a coortin', Mary Jane,
Tha's been a coortin', Mary Jane,
Tha's been a coortin', Mary Jane.
    On Ilkley Moor baht 'at,
    On Ilkley Moor baht 'at,
    On Ilkley Moor baht 'at.

3 Tha'll go and get thi deeath o' cowld,
    Chorus

4 Then we shall ha' to bury thee,
    Chorus

5 Then t'worms'll come an' ate thee oop,
    Chorus

6 Then t'ducks'll come an' ate oop t'worms,
    Chorus

7 Then we shall go an' ate oop t'ducks,
    Chorus

8 Then we shall all 'ave etten thee,
    Chorus

9 That's wheear we gets our oahn back,
    Chorus

Ould John Braddlum

Words and music anon.

This is an action song similar to *This Old Man* and *Ten Green Bottles*.

2 Number two, number two;
   Some boots pinch so gie I a shoe;
   Wi' a rum-tum-taddle-um,
   Ould John Braddlum,
   Hey, what country folk we be.

3 Number three, number three;
   Some loikes coffee and some loikes tea;
   Chorus

4 Number fowre, number fowre;
   Some says nowt but thinks the mowre;
   Chorus

5 Number foive, number foive;
   Old folks die when they can't stop aloive;
   Chorus

6 Number six, number six;
   Some use crutches when they can't use sticks;
   Chorus

7 Number seven, number seven;
   Much about t'same as number eleven;
   Chorus

8 Number eight, number eight;
   Some loikes a door but I loikes a gate;
   Chorus

9 Number nine, number nine;
   Some drinks beer 'cos they can't get wine;
   Chorus

10 Number ten, number ten;
    There bean't no women where there bean't no men;
    Chorus

11 Number eleven, number eleven;
    Much about t'same as number seven;
    Chorus

12 Number twelve, number twelve;
    If you wants any mowre you can sing it yerselves;
    Chorus

Polly Oliver

Words and music anon.

This song was included in William Chappell's *Popular Music of the Olden Time* (1859). He says, 'This is an old ballad entitled *Polly Oliver's Ramble'*.

1. As sweet Polly Oliver lay musing in bed, A sudden strange fancy came into her head; 'Nor father nor mother shall make me false prove! I'll list for a soldier and follow my love!'

2 So early next morning she softly arose,
   And dressed herself up in her dead brother's clothes;
   She cut her hair close and she stained her face brown,
   And went for a soldier to fair London Town.

3 Then up spake the Sergeant one day at his drill:
   'Now who's good at nursing? a captain lies ill!'
   'I'm ready,' says Polly; to nurse him she's gone,
   And finds 'tis her true love all wasted and wan.

4 The first week the doctor kept shaking his head;
   'No nursing, young fellow, can save him,' he said,
   But when Polly Oliver had nursed back his life,
   He cried, 'You have cherished him as if you were his wife!'

5 Oh then Polly Oliver, she burst into tears,
   And told the good doctor her hopes and her fears;
   And very soon after, for better for worse,
   The Captain took joyfully his pretty soldier nurse.

The Rio Grande

This famous sea song is a windlass and capstan shanty collected by Sir Richard Runciman Terry and published in 1921. It follows the form of solo and chorus.

pret-ty young gel, For we're bound for the Ri - o Grande.___ 2. Sing Grande.

2 Sing goodbye to Sally, and goodbye to Sue,
  Oh Rio,
  Sing goodbye to Sally, and goodbye to Sue,
  And we're bound for the Rio Grande.
  Then away love, away,
  'Way down Rio,
  And you who are listening, goodbye to you,
  And we're bound for the Rio Grande.

3 Our ship went sailing out over the bar,
  Oh Rio,
  Our ship went sailing out over the bar,
  And we're bound for the Rio Grande.
  Then away love, away,
  'Way down Rio,
  And we pointed her nose to the South-er-en Star
  And we're bound for the Rio Grande.

4 I said farewell to Kitty my dear,
  Oh Rio,
  I said farewell to Kitty my dear,
  And we're bound for the Rio Grande.
  Then away love, away,
  'Way down Rio,
  And she waved her white hand as we passed the south pier,
  And we're bound for the Rio Grande.

5 The oak and the ash and the bonny birk tree,
  Oh Rio,
  The oak and the ash and the bonny birk tree,
  And we're bound for the Rio Grande.
  Then away love, away,
  'Way down Rio,
  They're all growing green in the North Countrie,
  And we're bound for the Rio Grande.

Robin Hood

Words and music anon.

This is one of the many ballads about the legendary English outlaw and popular hero. This tune appears in *Pammelia*, the first collection of vocal rounds, catches and canons published in England, in 1609.

Steadily

1. Ro - bin Hood, Ro - bin Hood, with Lit - tle John, Were

hid - ing in a tree. There they were watch - ing the

path through the for - est To see what they__ could see._____ hold.

2 Here comes the Sheriff of Nottingham Shire
  A-riding with his men;
  Carrying gold to the lord of the manor
  With horsemen nine or ten.

3 Robin Hood, Robin Hood, jumps from his bough
  And bids the Sheriff stand;
  'Out of my way!' cried the Sheriff so sharply,
  ''Tis I who give the command.'

4 Robin Hood, Robin Hood, blew on his horn
  To sound his warning call;
  Down from the trees in the forest came tumbling
  Little John and Merry Men all.

5 'Odds,' said the Sheriff to Robin Hood's men,
  'I pray you take the gold.'
  'Thank you good Sheriff,' upspake Little John
  'And what we have we'll hold.'

Rule Britannia

Words by James Thomson
Music by Thomas Arne

2 The nations not so blest as thee
  Must in their turn to tyrants fall;
  Must in their turn, must in their turn to tyrants fall;
  While thou shalt flourish, shalt flourish great and free,
  The dread and envy of them all.
      Rule, Britannia! Britannia, rule the waves,
      Britons never, never, never shall be slaves.

3 Still more majestic shalt thou rise,
  More dreadful from each foreign stroke;
  More dreadful from, more dreadful from each foreign stroke;
  As the loud blast, loud blast that tears the skies,
  Serves but to root thy native oak.
      Chorus

4 The Muses, still with freedom found,
  Shall to thy happy court repair;
  Shall to, shall to, shall to thy happy court repair;
  Blest Isle! with matchless, with matchless beauty crown'd,
  And manly hearts to guard the fair.
      Chorus

Sally In Our Alley

Words and music 18th century

This is one of the few love songs in the
collection.

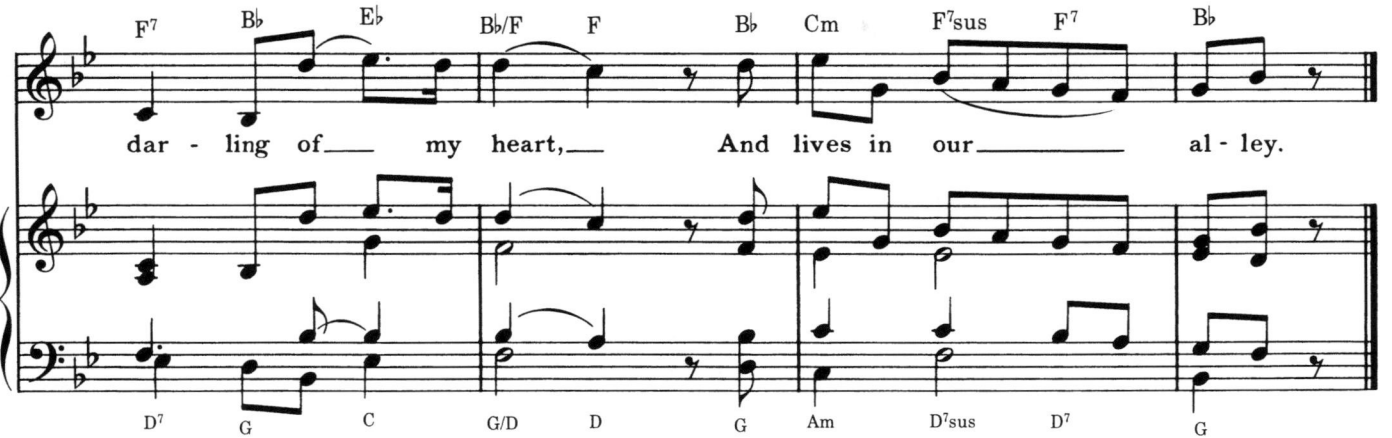

dar - ling of___ my heart,___ And lives in our_____ al - ley.

2 Of all the days are in the week,
   I dearly love but one day,
   And that's the day that comes betwixt
   A Saturday and Monday;
   O then I'm dressed all in my best,
   To walk abroad with Sally;
   She is the darling of my heart,
   And lives in our alley.

3 When Christmas comes about again,
   O then I shall have money;
   I'll save it up, and, box and all,
   I'll give it to my honey;
   And when my seven long years are out
   O then I'll marry Sally,
   And then how happily we'll live!
   But not in our alley.

Scarborough Fair

Words and music anon.

Paradoxes and riddles have frequently formed the subject of fireside stories and songs. This song is one of them. The original, according to Frank Kidson, is an old ballad called *The Elfin Knight*.

1. Are you go-ing to Scar-bo-rough Fair? Pars-ley, sage, rose-ma-ry and thyme; Re-mem-ber me to one who lives there____ For she was once a true love of mine. mine.

2 Tell her to make me a cambric shirt,
    Parsley, sage, rosemary and thyme;
    Without any seam or needlework,
    And then she'll be a true love of mine.

3 Tell her to wash it in yonder dry well,
    Parsley, sage, rosemary and thyme;
    Where water ne'er sprung, nor drop of rain fell,
    And then she'll be a true love of mine.

4 Tell her to dry it on yonder thorn,
    Parsley, sage, rosemary and thyme;
    Which never bore blossom since Adam was born,
    And then she'll be a true love of mine.

5 O, will you find me an acre of land,
    Parsley, sage, rosemary and thyme;
    Between the sea foam and the sea sand,
    Or never be a true lover of mine.

6 O, will you plough it with one lamb's horn,
    Parsley, sage, rosemary and thyme;
    And sow it all over with one peppercorn,
    Or never be a true lover of mine.

7 O, will you reap it with a sickle of leather,
    Parsley, sage, rosemary and thyme;
    And tie it all up with a peacock's feather,
    Or never be a true lover of mine.

8 And when you have done and finished your work,
    Parsley, sage, rosemary and thyme;
    Then come to me for your cambric shirt,
    And you shall be a true lover of mine.

Song of the Western Men

Words and music anon.

Sir Jonathan Trelawney, the Bishop of Bristol and Exeter, was committed to the Tower of London in 1688 by James II. Cornishmen then began marching to London to demand his release: this song resounded throughout Cornwall when their aim was achieved.

2 Out spake their captain brave and bold,
   A merry wight was he:
   'If London Tower were Michael's Hold,
   We'll set Trelawney free!
   We'll cross the Tamar, land to land,
   The Severn is no stay,
   With 'One and all,' and hand in hand,
   And who shall bid us nay?'
      A good sword and a trusty hand!
      A merry heart and true!
      King James's men shall understand
      What Cornish lads can do.

3 'And when we come to London Wall,
   A pleasant sight to view,
   Come forth! come forth, ye cowards all,
   Here's men as good as you!
   Trelawney he's in keep and hold,
   Trelawney he may die;
   But twenty thousand Cornish bold
   Will know the reason why!'
      Chorus

Sweet and Low

Words by Alfred, Lord Tennyson
Music by Joseph Barnaby

While my lit - tle one, while my pret - ty one sleeps._____

2 Sleep and rest, sleep and rest,
  Father will come to thee soon.
  Rest, rest on mother's breast,
  Father will come to thee soon;
  Father will come to his babe in the nest,
  Silver sails all out of the west,
  Under the silver moon,
  Sleep my little one, sleep, my pretty one, sleep.

The Vicar of Bray

Words and music 18th century

The vicar of the title managed to keep his position through the reigns of a succession of variously Roman Catholic and Protestant monarchs (Henry VIII, Edward VI, Mary and Elizabeth I). There were probably many other clergymen who were equally adaptable during that period!

1. In good King Charles's gold-en days, When loy-al-ty no harm meant, A zea-lous High Church-man was I, And so I got pre-fer-ment, To teach my flock I ne-ver missed, Kings were by God ap-point-ed, And lost are they that dare re-sist, Or touch the Lord's a-

CHORUS

-noint - ed. *And this is law, that I'll main-tain, Un - til my_ dy - ing_ day, Sir, That what-so - e - ver King may reign, I will be the Vi-car of Bray, Sir!*

2 When royal James possessed the crown
And Pop'ry grew in fashion,
The penal laws I hooted down
And read the Declaration;
The Church of Rome I found would fit
Full well my constitution,
And I had been a Jesuit,
But for the Revolution.
And this is the law, that I'll maintain
Until my dying day, Sir,
That whatsoever King may reign
I will be the Vicar of Bray, Sir!

3 When William was our King declared,
To ease the nation's grievance,
With this new wind about I steered
And swore to him allegiance.
Old principles I did revoke,
Set conscience at a distance,
And passive obedience was a joke,
A jest was non-resistance.
Chorus

4 When George in pudding time came o'er,
And moderate men looked big, sir,
I turned a cat-in-pan once more,
And so became a Whig, sir;
And thus preferment I procured
From our new Faith's defender,
And almost every day abjured
The Pope and the Pretender.
Chorus

5 The illustrious house of Hanover
And Protestant succession,
To these I do allegiance swear,
While they can keep possession;
For in my faith and loyalty
I never more will falter,
And George my lawful King shall be –
Until the times do alter.
Chorus

The Water of Tyne

Words and music anon.

This beautiful Northumbrian folk song is in the same vein as *Maa Bonny Lad*, except that it is the River Tyne that separates the lovers in this song.

2 Oh where is the boatman, my bonny hinny!
  Oh where is the boatman, bring him to me;
  To ferry me over the Tyne to my honey,
  And I will remember the boatman and thee.

3 Oh bring me a boatman, I'll give any money,
  And you for your trouble rewarded shall be;
  To ferry me over the Tyne to my honey,
  Or scull him across that rough river to me.

What Shall We Do With the Drunken Sailor?

This famous and popular song is a windlass and capstan shanty collected by Sir Richard Runciman Terry.

2 Put him in the long-boat until he's sober,
  Put him in the long-boat until he's sober,
  Put him in the long-boat until he's sober,
  Early in the morning.
  Hooray and up she rises,
  Hooray and up she rises,
  Hooray and up she rises,
  Early in the morning.

3 Pull out the plug and wet him all over, *etc.*
  Chorus

4 Put him in the scuppers with the hosepipe on him, *etc.*
  Chorus

Wididdicombe Fair

This Devonshire folk song was collected by the Reverend Sabine Baring-Gould. Widecombe-in-the-Moor is a picturesque village in a high fold of Dartmoor. Widecombe Fair is held on the second Tuesday in September.

90

Un - cle Tom Cob - leigh and all, _____ Old Un - cle Tom Cob - leigh and

all.' _____ 2 And all.' _____

2 'And when shall I see again my grey mare?'
All along, down along, out along lee,
'By Friday soon, or Saturday noon,'
    Wi' Bill Brewer, Jan Stewer, Peter
    Gurney,
    Peter Davy, Dan'l Whiddon, Harry
    Hawke,
    Old Uncle Tom Cobleigh and all,
    Old Uncle Tom Cobleigh and all.

3 Then Friday came, and Saturday noon,
All along, down along, out along lee,
But Tom Pearce's old mare hath not trotted
    home,
    Chorus

4 So Tom Pearce he go up to the top o' the hill,
All along, down along, out along lee,
And he seed his old mare down a-making her
    will,
    Chorus

5 So Tom Pearce's old mare, her took sick and
    died,
All along, down along, out along lee,
And Tom he sat down on a stone, and he
    cried,
    Chorus

6 But this isn't the end of this shocking affair,
All along, down along, out along lee,
Nor, though they be dead, of the horrid
    career,
    Chorus: Of Bill Brewer ...

7 When the wind whistles cold on the moor
    of a night,
All along, down along, out along lee,
Tom Pearce's old mare doth appear, ghastly
    white,
    Chorus: Wi' Bill Brewer ...

8 And all the long night be heard skirling and
    groans,
All along, down along, out along lee,
From Tom Pearce's old mare and a rattling of
    bones,
    Chorus: Of Bill Brewer ...

Windy Old Weather

Words and music anon.

This fishing song comes from the Norfolk coastal village of Happisburgh (pronounced as in verse 1), which has a lighthouse.

Strongly

1. As we were a-fish-ing off Hais-bor-ough Light, Shoot-ing and haul-ing and trawl-ing all night, It was wind-y old weath-er, storm-y old weath-er. When the wind blows, we all pull to-geth-er.

2 We sighted a herring, the king of the sea,
 Says, 'Now, old skipper, you cannot catch me.'
  In this windy old weather, stormy old weather,
  When the wind blows, we all pull together.

3 We sighted a mackerel with stripes on his back.
 'Time now, old skipper, to shift your main tack.'
  Chorus

4 We sighted a conger as long as a mile.
 'Wind's blowing easterly,' he said with a smile.
  Chorus

5 We sighted a plaice that had spots on his side.
 Says, 'Now, old skipper, these seas you won't ride.'
  Chorus

6 I think what these fishes are saying is right.
 We'll haul in our nets and we'll make for the light.
  Chorus

The Wraggle Taggle Gypsies

Words and music anon.

The romantic notion of the highborn lady running off with the gypsies is a very popular subject and appears in various forms in the many versions of this song.

1. Three gip - sies stood at the cas - tle gate. They sang so high, they— sang so low, The la - dy sate in her cham - ber late, Her heart it melt - ed a - way like snow.

94

2 They sang so sweet, they sang so shrill,
   That fast her tears began to flow,
   And she laid down her silken gown,
   Her golden rings and all her show.

3 She pluckéd off her high-heeled shoes,
   A-made of Spanish leather, O!
   She would in the street in her bare, bare feet,
   All out in the wind and the weather, O!

4 O saddle to me my milk-white steed,
   And go and fetch my pony, O!
   That I may ride and seek my bride,
   Who is gone with the wraggle taggle
      gypsies, O!

5 O he rode high, and he rode low,
   He rode through wood and copses too,
   Until he came to an open field,
   And there he espied his lady, O!

6 What makes you leave your house and land,
   Your golden treasure for to go?
   What makes you leave your new-wedded
      lord,
   To follow the wraggle taggle gypsies, O!

7 What care I for my house and land?
   What care I for my treasure, O?
   What care I for my new-wedded lord?
   I'm off with the wraggle taggle gypsies, O!

8 Last night you slept on a goose-feather bed,
   With the sheet turned down so bravely, O!
   And tonight you'll sleep in a cold open field,
   Along with the wraggle taggle gypsies, O!

9 What care I for a goose-feather bed,
   With the sheet turned down so bravely, O!
   For tonight I shall sleep in a cold open field,
   Along with the wraggle taggle gypsies, O!

Printed by Halstan:
Halstan UK, 2-10 Plantation Road, Amersham, Bucks, HP6 6HJ. United Kingdom
Halstan DE, Weißliliengasse 4, 55116 Mainz. Germany